AQA
GCSE Biology
Lab Book

Contents

Published by Pearson Education Limited, 80 Strand, London, WC2R 0RL.
www.pearsonschoolsandfecolleges.co.uk

Text © Mark Levesley, Sue Kearsey, and Pearson Education Limited 2018
Series editor: Stella Paes
Designed by Pete Stratton, Pearson Education Ltd.
Typeset by Servis Filmsetting Ltd.
Original illustrations © Pearson Education Limited 2018
Cover design by Pete Stratton
Cover photo/illustration © Shutterstock: Dirk Ercken

First published 2017
Second edition 2018

19
10 9 8 7 6 5 4 3

British Library Cataloguing in Publication Data
A catalogue record for this book is available from the British Library

ISBN 9781292267807

Acknowledgements
The publishers would like to thank Linda Turner for her contributions to this resource and would like to thank John Kavanagh for his contributions to the previous edition.
The rights of Mark Levesley and Sue Kearsey to be identified as authors of this work have been asserted by them in accordance with the Copyright, Designs and Patents Act 1988.

Notes from the publisher
We have attempted to identify all the recognised hazards in the practical activities in this guide. The Lab Book and online Technician's notes provide suitable warnings about the hazards and suggests appropriate precautions. Teachers and technicians should remember, however, that where there is a hazard, the employer is required to carry out a risk assessment under either the COSHH Regulations or the Management of Health and Safety at Work Regulations. We have assumed that practical work is carried out in a properly equipped and maintained laboratory and that any fieldwork takes account of the employer's guidelines. In particular, we have assumed that any mains-operated electrical equipment is properly maintained, that students have been shown how to conduct normal laboratory operations (such as heating or handling heavy objects) safely and that good practice is observed when chemicals or living organisms are handled. We have also assumed that classes are sufficiently small and well-behaved for a teacher to be able to exercise adequate supervision of the students and that rooms are not so crowded that students' activities pose a danger to their neighbours.
Science safety experts have reviewed but not trialled this text. Following receipt of the reviews any guidance has been incorporated and the resources updated.

Important note

Neither Pearson, the authors nor the series editor take responsibility for the safety of any activity.
Before doing any practical activity you are legally required to carry out your own risk assessment. In particular, any local rules issued by your employer must be obeyed, regardless of what is recommended in this resource. Where students are required to write their own risk assessments they must always be checked by the teacher and revised, as necessary, to cover any issues the students may have overlooked. The teacher should always have the final control as to how the practical is conducted.
Further sources of information: CLEAPSS, www.cleapss.org.uk (includes Secondary Science Laboratory Handbook and Hazcards).

Specification note
This resource is based on the April 2016 accredited version of the specification. The worksheets in this resource have not been reviewed or endorsed by AQA and should not be considered as being published by AQA. Copies of official specifications for all AQA qualifications may be found on the website: www.aqa.org.uk.
While the Publishers have made every attempt to ensure that advice on the qualification and its assessment is accurate, the official specification and associated assessment guidance materials are the only authoritative source of information and should always be referred to for definitive guidance.

Content accuracy
Pearson has robust editorial processes, including answer and fact checks, to ensure the accuracy of the content in this publication, and every effort is made to ensure this publication is free of errors. We are, however, only human, and occasionally errors do occur. Pearson is not liable for any misunderstandings that arise as a result of errors in this publication, but it is our priority to ensure that the content is accurate. If you spot an error, please do contact us at resourcescorrections@pearson.com so we can make sure it is corrected.

This Biology practical workbook is designed to enrich and deepen your understanding of AQA GCSE Science through each of the required practical activities.

We want you to enjoy your science lessons and at the same time feel that you are well-prepared for your final examinations.

Each practical is not a recipe to be merely followed but a step-by-step guide with thought-provoking questions. Each practical can be adapted to suit your school.

The Lab Book provides a clear individual record of practical work linked to the AQA required practical activities.

(Your teacher can also download a practical tracking document from **www.pearsonschools.co.uk/AQApracticalsupport** for your whole class too.)

Working though this book should:

- Further develop your practical confidence and competence in using a wide range of apparatus and techniques.
- Support you to work carefully and methodically.
- Improve your experimental skills and strategies for planning and adapting laboratory procedures.
- Show you the link between doing practical work and applying your knowledge and understanding of scientific ideas.
- Encourage your use of the language of experimentation, so that you can use words like validity, precision and reproducibility with accuracy and confidence.
- Provide practice in answering new practically-based GCSE questions designed to test the full range of your abilities.
- Support you to 'Work Scientifically'.
  (We recommend that you find out more about what AQA means by checking your specification.)

Working Scientifically and the use of apparatus and techniques is assessed across all of your GCSE Science papers. Examiners will expect you to have completed all of these practical activities yourself and will test what you have learned in a number of ways.

Some examples of the style of the questions you might be asked have been added to each practical activity.

They may ask you to:

- Show what you know about these experiments. (Assessment Objective 1)
- Apply what you know about Working Scientifically and test how well you present and analyse data. (Assessment Objective 2)
- Make sense of results, question evidence, suggest improvements and develop conclusions. (Assessment Objective 3)

This book will help you practise and improve your mathematical skills in science too, especially your use of graphs, equations and how you analyse your results.

We hope that these experiments will trigger your curiosity about science, the scientific process and how scientists perform investigations. We encourage you to ask deeper questions and carry out further investigations, with your teacher's consent.

Stella Paes
Series Editor

Having an investigative mind and carrying out experiments are fundamental to science. The AQA science curricuum has carefully selected practical work to:

- enhance the delivered content
- increase enthusiasm for the subject
- promote a more scientifically literate society
- enable students to gain vital transferable skills.

Completing these required practicals, along with other investigations selected by your teacher, enables you to have a rich hands-on experience of science as it is meant to be – a dynamic, practical subject relevant to everyone.

This Lab Book has been designed to support your practical work, giving you all the instructions you need to perform the required practicals, including apparatus and techniques (AT) skills self-assessment so that you can track your progress.

Every effort has been made to ensure you have the opportunity to cover all of the specification skills (WS – Working scientifically, AT – Use of apparatus and techniques). However, because we provide you with the methods, you will not be carrying out a full investigation (WS 2.2).

It is hoped that these required practicals will be supplemented by other investigations and experiments that you will complete through your GCSE course. However you could carry out your own plan, or adapt your plan using the methods presented in this book. Again, plans need to be risked assessed.

Each practical activity has:

- **Practical Objectives**, which are what you should do that relate directly to the AQA required practical activities.
- **Content Objectives**, which are what you should know and understand from the AQA specification that relate directly to this practical.
- **Learning Outcomes**, which are a way for you to track your mastery of key apparatus and techniques.

Biology

One of the first people to examine cells using a microscope was Robert Hooke. He examined bark from a cork oak tree and saw little box shapes. He called them 'cells' because he thought the boxes looked like the small rooms (or cells) found in monasteries at the time. Hooke realised that it was important to make accurate drawings of what he saw to help explain his work to others. You are going to examine specimens using a microscope and then make labelled drawings of them.

Your teacher may watch to see if you can:

- handle microscopes and slides carefully and safely.

Core learning outcomes: I am able to…
use appropriate apparatus to record length and area
use a microscope to make observations of biological specimens and produce labelled scientific drawings.

Method 1: Examining pre-prepared slides of cells

A Set up your microscope on the lowest magnification objective lens. Work out the total magnification and measure the diameter of the field of view (by using the microscope to observe a transparent ruler). Record this in the box below.

B Put the next most powerful objective lens in place. Work out the magnification and by how much it has increased from the magnification in step **A** (e.g. moving from a ×10 to a ×50 lens is an increase of 5 times). Now divide the diameter of the field of view from step **A** by the increase in magnification to give you the new diameter of the field of view (e.g. if the field of view in step **A** was 2 mm, then 2 ÷ 5 = 0.4 mm). Do this for each objective lens. Record the total magnification and field of view diameter for each objective lens in the box below.

Practical Objective

To use a microscope to observe cells and sub-cellular structures.

Content Objective

The light microscope allows observation of plant and animal cells and can be used to estimate relative size of cells and some sub-cellular structures.

Apparatus

- light microscope
- lamp
- prepared slides
- transparent ruler

Safety

- Handle slides with care.

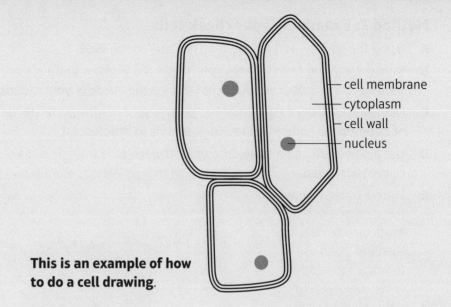

C Now go back to the lowest magnification objective lens and observe a prepared slide.

D Use higher magnifications to observe the cells. Estimate the sizes using your field of view diameters.

E Using a sharp pencil, draw four or five cells in the box below. Identify and label the cells' parts using straight ruled lines. Add the magnification and any sizes that you have estimated.

— cell membrane
— cytoplasm
— cell wall
— nucleus

This is an example of how to do a cell drawing.

Method 2: Examining your cheek cells

A   Using the pipette, add a small drop of water to the slide.

B   Stroke the inside of your cheek gently with the wooden spatula. You only want to collect loose cells, so do not scratch the inside of your mouth.

C   Use the end of the spatula that has been in your mouth to stir the drop of water on the slide. Place the used spatula in disinfectant.

D   Use a pipette to add a small drop of methylene blue stain. This makes cells easier to see.

E   Place a coverslip onto the slide at a 45° angle on one edge of the drop. Then use a toothpick to gently lower the coverslip onto the drop, as shown in the diagram. Avoid trapping air bubbles, which will appear as black-edged circles under a microscope.

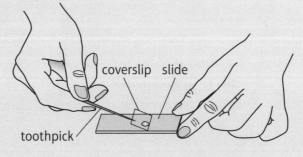

F   Touch a piece of paper towel to any liquid that spreads out from under the coverslip.

G   Use the lowest magnification objective lens to observe the slide. The **nuclei** of the cheek cells will be dark blue.

H   Use higher magnifications to observe the cells. Estimate the sizes using your field of view diameters.

I   Using a sharp pencil, draw two or three cells in the box below. Identify and label the cells' parts using straight ruled lines. Add the magnification and any sizes that you have estimated.

Apparatus

- light microscope
- lamp
- microscope slide
- coverslip
- methylene blue stain
- pipette
- paper towel
- water
- wooden toothpick/ cocktail stick
- sterile wooden spatula/ tongue depressor
- disinfectant

Safety

- Handle slides with care.
- Anything that you have put into your mouth should be placed in disinfectant after use.
- Wear gloves if using stains.
- Wear eye protection.

Method 3: Examining onion cells

A Use a pipette to add a drop of iodine solution to a microscope slide.

B Using forceps, remove a very small piece of the thin 'skin' on the inside of the fleshy part of the onion. It is quite tricky to handle as it is very thin.

C Place the small piece of skin on the drop of iodine on the slide.

D Place a coverslip onto the slide at a 45° angle on one edge of the drop. Then use a toothpick to gently lower the coverslip onto the drop, as shown in the diagram. Avoid trapping air bubbles, which will appear as black-edged circles under a microscope.

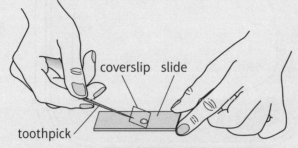
coverslip   slide
toothpick

E Touch a piece of paper towel to any liquid that spreads out from under the coverslip.

F Use the lowest magnification objective lens to observe the slide. Then use higher magnifications to observe the cells in more detail. Estimate sizes as you observe.

G Using a sharp pencil, draw four or five cells in the box below. Identify and label the cells using straight ruled lines. Add the magnification and any sizes that you have estimated.

Apparatus

- light microscope
- lamp
- microscope slide
- coverslip
- iodine stain
- pipette
- paper towel
- forceps
- wooden toothpick/cocktail stick
- piece of onion bulb
- gloves

Safety

- Handle slides and microscopes with care.
- Wear gloves if using stains.
- Wear eye protection.

Exam-style questions

01 The diagram shows a plant cell viewed under a light microscope.

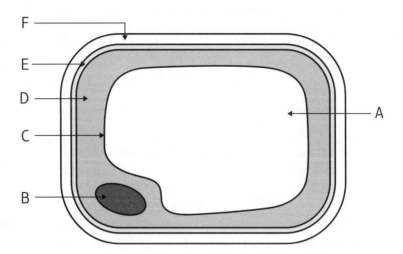

01.1 Which letters label the following structures? **[2 marks]**

Cell wall ☐ Cytoplasm ☐

01.2 The cell is taken from the root of the plant.

If the cell were taken from a leaf, which other sub-cellular structure would you expect to see under a light microscope? **[1 mark]**

01.3 The plant cell is 0.1 mm wide. A student estimates that the length of the nucleus is a sixth of the length of the cell.

Calculate the length of the nucleus. Give your answer in micrometres (μm) and to 3 significant figures. **[3 marks]**

Answer _____ μm

01.4 Bacterial cells are much smaller than plant cells.

A bacterial cell measures 2.6×10^3 nm. What does the cell measure in μm? **[1 mark]**

Answer _____ μm

Microbial cultures (for example, of certain bacteria) are used to study the effects of plant extracts, antibiotics and antiseptics. (Antiseptics are substances used to kill microorganisms on the surface of the body or on equipment.) In this kind of investigation it is important to work aseptically so that the substances are only tested against one organism and the results are not spoiled by other microorganisms.

Your teacher may watch to see if you can:
- work safely and aseptically with microorganisms.

Core learning outcomes: I am able to…
use appropriate apparatus to record length and area
use appropriate apparatus and techniques to observe and measure the process of bacterial growth
safely and ethically use bacteria to measure physiological function and response to antibiotics and antiseptics in the environment
use appropriate techniques and qualititative reagents in problem-solving contexts to find the best antibiotic to use or the best concentration of antiseptic to use.

Method
Pouring an agar plate
A Keeping the lid on the Petri dish, turn the dish upside down. Use the pen to draw three sections on the base, as shown in the diagram in the safety box. Label one section 'control' and label the other two sections with the name or concentration of each antiseptic. Add your initials and the date near the edge of the dish. Turn the dish the right way up.

B Light the Bunsen burner and set it to a roaring flame.

C Work with a partner to pour the plate. One student should unscrew the cap of the nutrient agar bottle and quickly pass the glass neck of the bottle through the Bunsen flame, as shown in the diagram below. The other student should lift the lid of the Petri dish just enough to allow the first student to pour the agar carefully into the dish. Pour in enough agar to half fill the depth of the Petri dish base. Replace the dish lid immediately. Flame the open neck of the agar bottle again before screwing the cap back on.

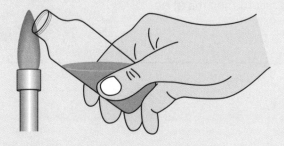

D Leave the agar to solidify.

Practical Objective

To investigate the effect of antiseptics on bacteria.

Content Objective

Aseptic technique is used to grow uncontaminated bacterial cultures. Calculating the area of clear zones around antiseptic discs can be used to determine the effect of antiseptics on bacteria.

Apparatus

- Petri dish with lid
- screw top bottle of sterile nutrient agar, melted and kept liquid in a water bath until needed
- bacterial culture in screw-top bottle
- sterile pipette in wrapper
- sterile spreader in wrapper
- beaker of disinfectant
- two small filter paper discs of different antiseptic concentration or type
- small disc of sterile filter paper
- sticky tape
- marker pen
- forceps
- ruler
- Bunsen burner and heat-resistant mat

Making a bacterial plate

E Remove the pipette from its wrapper and do not put it down.

F Unscrew the cap of the bottle of bacterial culture and quickly pass the neck of the bottle through the Bunsen flame.

G Draw a small amount of culture into the pipette then flame the neck of the bottle again and replace the lid. Do not put the pipette down while you are doing this.

H Lift the lid of the Petri dish as little as possible and gently add two drops of culture to the agar. Replace the dish lid and place the pipette in disinfectant.

I Unwrap the spreader and use it to gently spread the culture drops across the agar using a back-and-forwards motion. Ensure you only lift the Petri dish as little as possible while doing this.

J Replace the dish lid and place the spreader in disinfectant.

Adding antiseptic discs

K Sterilise the forceps by quickly passing them through the Bunsen flame.

L Use the forceps to pick up the sterile filter paper disc. Lift the dish lid just enough so that the forceps do not touch the bacterial layer on the agar in the dish, and carefully place the disc on the section labelled 'control'. Replace the dish lid as quickly as possible.

M Sterilise the forceps as before (step **K**). Then repeat step **L** with one of the antiseptic discs, placing it on the appropriate section of agar. Remember to replace the dish lid as quickly as possible.

N Repeat step **M** with the other antiseptic disc.

O Tape the lid onto your Petri dish with two pieces of tape, as shown in the Safety box, and invert the dish. Leave it at 20–25 °C for two to three days.

P Look carefully at your dish. **Do not open it**.

Recording your results

1 Measure the diameter of the circle around each disc where there is no bacterial growth, as shown in the diagram opposite.

2 Divide each diameter by 2 to calculate the radius (r) for each circle. Then calculate the area of no bacterial growth using the formula area = πr^2.

3 In the space below, draw and complete a table to record the area of no bacterial growth for each disc.

Safety

- This work requires aseptic working.
- Plates must be taped closed as shown in the diagram below. This allows air in and does not encourage the growth of pathogenic bacteria.

- Dispose of all cultures and equipment safely, as instructed by your teacher.
- Take care to avoid burning your fingers when flaming the neck of an agar bottle.
- Avoid touching eyes or skin after handling bacterial cultures. Wash splashes immediately with water and soap.
- Wash hands thoroughly with soap and water before the practical and again before leaving the laboratory.

diameter of zone with no bacterial growth

Considering your results/conclusions

4 Explain what your results show about the effect of antiseptics on bacteria.

5 Compare your results with those of other groups.

   a Did other groups get the same results? If not, suggest why not.

   b Explain which of the discs was the most effective at killing bacteria.

Evaluation

6 Suggest a way in which the method could be improved, and give a reason for your suggestion.

7 **a** Identify steps in the method that contributed to working aseptically.

   b Explain the importance of working aseptically in this practical.

Exam-style questions

01 A company has produced a new antiseptic handwash. The handwash can be diluted to give different concentrations.

This is the method used.

   1. The scientists rub their hands with the 0% concentration of handwash.

   2. The scientists make a thumbprint on a sterile agar plate.

   3. After incubation, the scientists count the colonies of bacteria that grew on the agar plate.

4. The scientists repeat the test twice more using the 0% concentration, until they have taken three measurements.

5. The experiment is repeated for 25%, 50%, 75% and 100% concentrations.
   The results are in the table below.

Percentage concentration of handwash	Number of bacterial colonies			
	Test 1	Test 2	Test 3	Mean
0	46	52	48	49
25	40	39	41	40
50	27	29	25	27
75	11	10	9	10
100	0	0	0	0

01.1 What was the independent variable in this study? **[1 mark]**

01.2 Which of the concentrations of handwash was the experimental control? **[1 mark]**

01.3 Why did the scientists use an experimental control? **[1 mark]**

01.4 A scientist examined the results in the table and decided there were no anomalous results.
Explain how the scientist made this decision. **[1 mark]**

01.5 Hospitals must keep their costs down. They asked for further tests to be carried out in order to discover the lowest concentration of handwash that will kill all the bacteria.
Suggest a range of concentrations that the scientists should test. **[1 mark]**

01.6 Explain why you chose the range of concentrations in your answer to question **01.5**. **[1 mark]**

The cells in a potato contain many substances dissolved in water. The cells are surrounded by cell membranes that are permeable to water. When a strip of potato is placed in a solution, the overall movement of water molecules between the potato cells and the solution will depend on which has the higher concentration of solutes. In this practical, you will investigate osmosis in potato strips in terms of the percentage change in mass of potato in different solutions.

Your teacher may watch to see if you can:

- measure accurately
- work carefully.

Core learning outcomes: I am able to…
use appropriate apparatus to record mass and time
use appropriate apparatus and techniques to observe and measure the process of osmosis
measure the rate of osmosis by water uptake.

Method

A Using the waterproof pen, label each tube with the name of one of the solutions. Place the boiling tubes in the rack, as shown in the diagram.

B Dry a potato strip carefully by blotting it with a paper towel. Measure its mass on the balance.

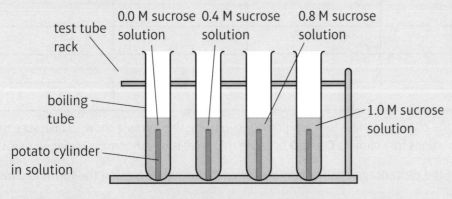

C Place the potato strip into one of the tubes. Record the concentration of sucrose solution and the mass of the strip in your results table (see next page).

D Repeat steps **B** and **C** until all strips have been measured and placed in tubes.

E Carefully fill each tube with the appropriate solution, so the potato is fully covered. Leave the tubes for at least 30 minutes.

F Use the forceps to remove each potato strip from its tube, blot dry on a paper towel and measure its mass again. Record all the masses in the results table.

Practical Objective

To investigate how solution concentration affects percentage change in mass of potato strips due to osmosis.

Content Objective

Osmosis is the diffusion of water from a dilute solution to a concentrated solution through a partially permeable membrane.

Apparatus

- four potato strips
- accurate balance
- four boiling tubes and rack (or beakers)
- waterproof pen
- four sucrose solutions: 0.0 M, 0.4 M, 0.8 M and 1.0 M
- forceps
- paper towels

Safety

- Do not drink any of the solutions or eat the potatoes.

Prediction

1   For each of the solutions you will use, predict whether the potato strips will gain mass, lose mass or keep the same mass. Explain your predictions.

Recording your results

2   Complete the first three columns of the table below – Concentration of sucrose solution, **A** and **B** – with the solution descriptions and your measurements from the experiment.

Concentration of sucrose solution (M)	A Mass of potato strip at start (g)	B Mass of potato strip at end (g)	C Change in mass (g) = B – A	D % change in mass $= \frac{C}{A} \times 100\%$

3   Complete column **C** by calculating the change in mass for each potato strip using the formula shown. Make sure the sign is included when writing down values for columns **C** and **D** because this reveals whether mass is gained or lost.

4   Complete column **D** by calculating the percentage change in mass for each potato strip using the formula shown.

5   Compare the results for percentage change in mass from all the groups in the class. For each solution, identify any results that seem very different from the others (anomalous results).
    Try to suggest a reason why they are so different.

6 Excluding any anomalous results, calculate a mean value for percentage change in mass for each solution.

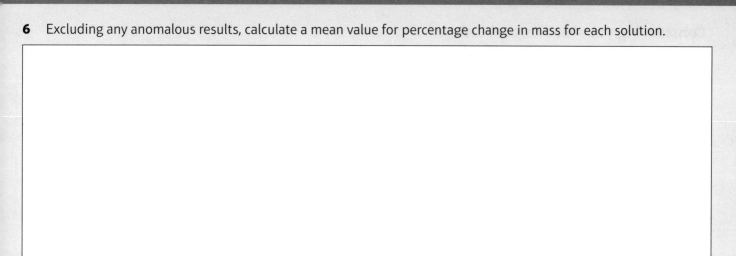

7 Draw a suitable chart or graph to show the mean percentage change in the mass of each potato strip (on the *y*-axis) against the concentration of sucrose solution (on the *x*-axis). Remember that your *y*-axis may need positive and negative numbers.

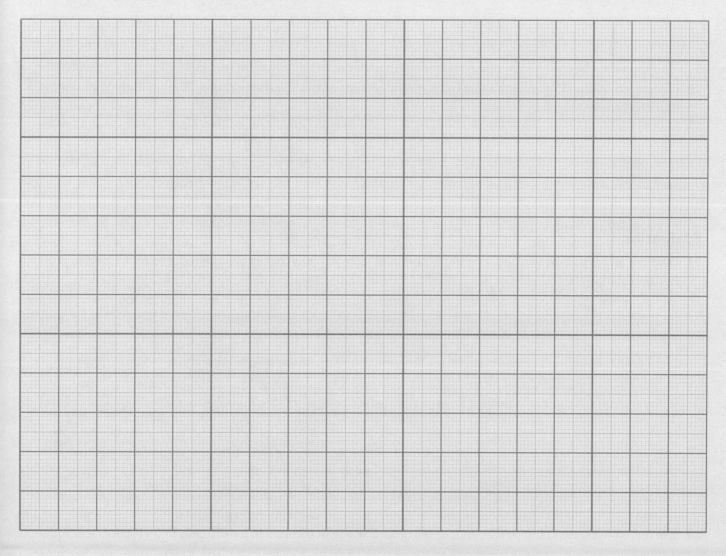

Considering your results/conclusions

8 Describe and explain the pattern shown in your chart or graph. Use the word 'osmosis' in your answer.

9 Explain why you calculated percentage change in mass.

10 Explain why calculating a mean value from several repeats of the same experiment is more likely to give a value that can be reproduced by others.

Evaluation

11 Describe any problems you had with the experiment. Suggest how these could be reduced or avoided to produce better results.

12 Explain how you could use your results to calculate the rate of osmosis in potato cells in 0.4 M sucrose solution.

Exam-style questions

01 Red blood cells were placed in different concentrations of sodium chloride. After two hours, the samples were examined to find the percentage of the cells that had burst. The results are shown in the table below.

Sodium chloride concentration (g/100 cm³)	0.32	0.36	0.40	0.44	0.48
Percentage of red blood cells that burst	100	90	44	15	0

01.1 The different concentrations were made by diluting a stock solution of sodium chloride of concentration 1.0 g/100 cm³ with distilled water.
Describe how to make 10 cm³ of 0.40 g/100 cm³ sodium chloride solution. **[2 marks]**

01.2 Explain why all the red blood cells burst when placed in the 0.32 g/100 cm³ sodium chloride solution. **[3 marks]**

01.3 Onion cells were placed in the same range of sodium chloride solutions. Explain why none of the onion cells burst. **[1 mark]**

01.4 If a kidney is diseased and not working, the person may be sent for dialysis. Waste materials from the blood diffuse across a partially permeable membrane into the dialysis fluid. The dialysis fluid has glucose and salts in it.
Suggest **two** problems that might occur if the dialysis fluid were pure water. **[2 marks]**

By law, all packaged food and drink must be labelled to show how much fat, sugar, protein and some other substances it contains. This is to help customers make informed choices about what they eat and drink. Every new food or drink that is developed must be tested to produce the information needed for the labelling. You will be given a range of powdered foods. Use the food tests below to identify whether each food contains the substances that the reagents test for. Use your results to help you identify the foods from the list you are given. Remember to wipe the spatula and stirrer clean between tests (using a paper towel) to prevent cross-contamination.

Your teacher may watch to see if you can:

- follow instructions carefully
- work safely, reducing the risk of harm from hazards.

Core learning outcomes: I am able to…
safely use a water bath and electric heater
use qualitative reagents to identify biological molecules.

Method

Iodine test for starch

A   Place one spatula of powdered food on a dish.

B   Using a dropper, place a few drops of iodine solution onto the food.

C   Record the name of the food and any change in the colour of the solution.

Benedict's test for reducing sugars

D   Place one spatula of powdered food into a test tube. Add about $1\,cm^3$ of water to the tube and stir to mix.

E   Add an equal volume of Benedict's solution and mix.

F   Place the tube in a water bath at about 95 °C for a few minutes.

G   Record the letter of the food and the colour of the solution.

Biuret test for protein

H   Place one spatula of powdered food into a test tube. Add about $1\,cm^3$ of water to the tube and stir to mix.

I   Add an equal volume of potassium hydroxide (Biuret B) solution to the tube and stir.

J   Add two drops of copper sulfate (Biuret A) solution and stir.

K   Record the name of the food and the colour of the solution after a few minutes.

Emulsion test for lipids

L   Place one spatula of powdered food into a test tube.

M   Add $2\,cm^3$ of ethanol to the tube. Place a bung firmly in the end of the tube and shake the tube vigorously.

N   Allow the contents to settle.

O   Pour the liquid from the top of the mixture into a test tube half filled with water.

P   Record the name of the food and whether the water is cloudy or clear.

Practical Objective

To identify starch, reducing sugars, proteins and lipids in foods.

Content Objective

The digestive system is a system in which several organs work together to break down large molecules into smaller, more soluble molecules so that they can be absorbed as food.

Apparatus

- eye protection
- water
- measuring cylinder
- spatula
- powdered foods
- paper towels
- test tubes, racks and bungs
- stirrer
- iodine solution in dropper bottle
- Benedict's solution
- potassium hydroxide (Biuret B) solution
- copper sulfate (Biuret A) solution
- ethanol
- cold water
- electric waterbath at 95 °C

Safety

- Wear eye protection.
- Wash any splashes from skin quickly.
- Do not taste any of the food substances.
- Ethanol (IDA) is hazardous, harmful and highly flammable. Keep it away from flames.
- Copper sulfate is poisonous and potassium hydroxide is corrosive (both substances are also present in Benedict's solution). Handle solutions with care and wipe up any spills.
- Avoid scalding with hot water.

Recording your results

1   Record your results in the table. There is space below the table to add more rows if needed.

Food	Colour at end of ...			
	iodine test	Benedict's test	Biuret test	emulsion test

Considering your results/conclusions

2   Which foods contained:

  a   starch

  b   reducing sugar

  c   protein

  d   lipid?

3   Do any of your tests give an indication of how much of a substance a food contains? Give a reason for your answer.

Evaluation

4   Identify any problems you had with this experiment. Explain how the method could be improved to reduce or avoid these errors.

Exam-style questions

01   A student has three bottles. All the labels have fallen off, but the three solutions are:

- starch
- amylase
- albumen (egg white).

The student does some tests on the solution in each bottle.

Test reagent	Final colour		
	Solution 1	**Solution 2**	**Solution 3**
Iodine	Blue/black	Yellow	Yellow
Biuret	Pale blue	Lilac	Lilac

01.1   The student decides that **solution 1** is the starch solution. Explain how this decision was made.   **[1 mark]**

01.2   The student mixes equal volumes of the starch solution with **solution 2** and **solution 3**, and incubates both mixtures at 37 °C for 20 minutes.

Test reagent	Final colour	
	Starch solution and solution 2 mixture	**Starch solution and solution 3 mixture**
Benedict's	Blue	Brick red

Identify what **solution 2** and **solution 3** are. Explain your decisions using evidence from both the results tables.   **[6 marks]**

Solution 2:

_____

Explanation:

_____

_____

_____

Solution 3:

_____

Explanation:

_____

_____

_____

Amylase is an enzyme made in the salivary glands in your mouth and in the pancreas. It catalyses the breakdown of starch into smaller sugar molecules. The iodine test identifies the presence of starch, but does not react with sugar. You will use this test to show how effective amylase is in digesting starch at different pHs.

Your teacher may watch to see if you can:

● work safely

● collect accurate data.

Core learning outcomes: I am able to…
use appropriate apparatus to record time, pH and the volumes of liquids
safely use a water bath
measure the rate of reaction by the colour change of iodine indicator
use qualitative iodine reagent to identify starch by continuous sampling.

Method

A Pipette one drop of iodine solution into each depression of the dimple tile.

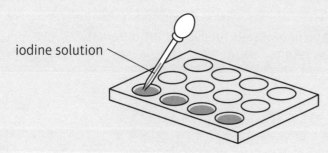

iodine solution

B Use a syringe to place 2 cm³ of amylase solution into a test tube.

C Add 1 cm³ of your pH solution to the test tube using a second syringe. Record the pH of the solution that you are using.

D Using a third syringe, add 2 cm³ of starch solution to a second test tube.

E Stand the test tubes from steps **B** and **D** in the water bath. When the liquid in the tubes reaches 30 °C, pour the starch solution into the amylase solution and start the stop clock. Use the pipette to stir the mixture.

F After 20 seconds, take a small amount of the mixture in the pipette and place one drop of it on the first iodine drop on the tile. Return the rest of the solution in the pipette to the test tube.

G If the iodine solution turns black, there is still starch in the mixture and you should repeat step **F** after 10 seconds. If the iodine solution remains yellow, all the starch has been digested and you should record the time taken for this to happen.

H If there is time, repeat the experiment using a solution with a different pH.

Practical Objective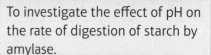

To investigate the effect of pH on the rate of digestion of starch by amylase.

Content Objective

Amylase is a carbohydrase enzyme that breaks down starch into soluble sugars.

Apparatus

● eye protection

● iodine solution in dropping bottle

● dimple tile

● test tubes

● test-tube rack

● syringes

● pipette

● amylase solution

● starch solution

● solutions of specific pH

● stop clock

● beaker of warm water at 30 °C to act as a water bath

● thermometer

Safety ⚠

● Wear eye protection.

Prediction

1   Predict at which pH the amylase will digest starch fastest. Explain your prediction.

Recording your results

2   Collect data from all of the groups in the class so you have results for each of the different pHs. Draw a table in the box below to present these results.

3   If you have more than one result for any pH, use the space below to calculate the mean time. Add the mean times to your results table.

Considering your results

4 In the space below, plot a line graph to show the time taken for amylase to digest starch at different pHs.

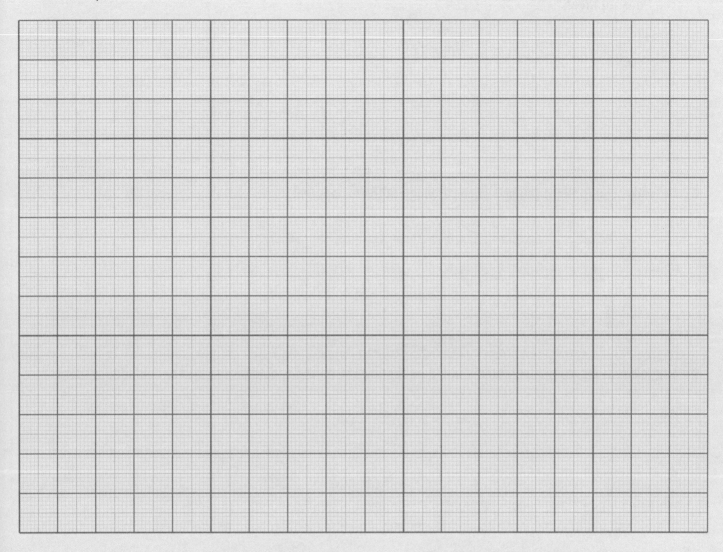

5 Use your graph to describe the effect of pH on the time taken for amylase to digest starch.

6 Suggest a reason for the shape of your graph.

7 Some tests are qualitative (they will only show whether the substance is present or not). Other tests are semi-quantitative (they will provide approximate values of how much might be present, e.g. 'little', 'some' or 'a lot'). In this practical, iodine solution was used to detect whether starch was present or not. Is this test qualitative or semi-quantitative?

Explain your answer.

_____

_____

_____

8 Describe any problems you had when carrying out the experiment.

_____

_____

_____

_____

9 Suggest reasons for these problems and ideas for how the method could be changed to help reduce them.

_____

_____

_____

_____

10 Are any of the results surprising? If so, why?

_____

_____

_____

_____

11 Do you think you have enough results to support your conclusion? Explain your answer.

_____

_____

_____

Exam-style questions

01 Pepsin is a protease enzyme produced by the stomach. When pepsin breaks down the protein in egg white, the egg white changes from cloudy to clear.

A student did an investigation into pepsin activity.

This is the method they used.

1. Put 1 cm³ water, 1 cm³ pepsin and 5 cm³ egg white in a test tube labelled **A**.
2. Put 2 cm³ water and 5 cm³ egg white in a test tube labelled **B**.
3. Leave test tubes **A** and **B** for 15 minutes and record the results.

01.1 Explain why the contents of tube **A** became clear after 15 minutes. **[1 mark]**

01.2 Explain why the contents of tube **B** stayed cloudy after 15 minutes. **[1 mark]**

01.3 Why did the student add water to tube **A**? **[1 mark]**

01.4 The student decides to investigate the effect of the concentration of pepsin on the rate of digestion of egg white. Explain how the student can vary the concentration of pepsin. **[1 mark]**

01.5 The student knows that temperature and pH also affect the rate of reaction of enzymes and that these variables should be controlled.

Suggest suitable values to use for pH and temperature. Give reasons for your choices and say how the student should control these variables. **[4 marks]**

pH value:

Reason for choice:

Method of control:

26

Temperature value:

Reason for choice:

Method of control:

Microscopic algae have cells that contain chloroplasts, like plant leaf cells. The algae can be trapped in jelly balls to make them easier to handle. You will put algal balls in an indicator that changes colour as carbon dioxide levels change. Under normal conditions the indicator is a red colour, but this changes to yellow at higher carbon dioxide concentrations and purple at lower carbon dioxide concentrations.[1]

Your teacher may watch to see if you can:

- follow instructions carefully
- work safely.

Core learning outcomes: I am able to…
use appropriate apparatus to record the rate of change in carbon dioxide levels and to measure and control the temperature of the water in the 'heat shield' beaker
safely use a thermometer to measure and control the temperature of the water in the 'heat shield' beaker
use appropriate apparatus and techniques to observe and measure the process of change of carbon dioxide levels
safely and ethically use and dispose of living algae
measure the rate of reaction by colour change of indicator according to pH.

Method

A Decide the different distances you are going to use between the algae and the lamp. You will need one clear glass bottle for each distance. You will also need one extra bottle.

B Add 10–15 algal balls to each bottle. (The same number of algal balls should be added to each bottle.)

C Add the same volume of indicator solution to each bottle and put on the bottle caps.

D Your teacher will have a chart or a range of bottles showing the colours of the indicator at different pHs. Compare the colour in your bottles with this pH range to work out the pH at the start.

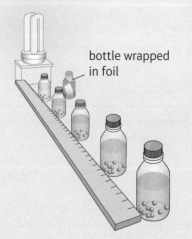

bottle wrapped in foil

E Set up a heat filter between the lamp and where you will place your bottles. The heat filter is a water-filled bottle or other clear container. Take great care not to spill water near the lamp. Set up a cardboard barrier on the three sides of the lamp that do not face the glass bottles.

F Cover one bottle in kitchen foil, so that it is in the dark.

G Place your bottles at measured distances from the lamp. Put the bottle covered in kitchen foil next to the bottle that is closest to the lamp.

H Turn on the lamp and time 60 minutes (or longer).

Practical Objective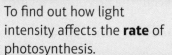

To find out how light intensity affects the **rate** of photosynthesis.

Content Objective

Photosynthesis is an endothermic reaction in which energy is transferred to chloroplasts by light. The rate of photosynthesis is affected by light intensity, carbon dioxide concentration and temperature.

Apparatus

- eye protection
- bijou bottles and caps
- beaker of algal balls
- hydrogencarbonate indicator
- high lumen output lamp (> 1000 lumen bulb) and heat filter
- metre rule
- measuring cylinder
- kitchen foil
- stop clock
- plastic forceps/spoon

Safety

- Wear eye protection.
- Wash your hands after setting up the experiment.
- Avoid touching the hot lamp.
- Using cardboard, shield the three sides of the lamp that do not face the glass bottles.

[1]A note to teachers: The full title of this required practical is 'Investigate the effect of light intensity on the rate of photosynthesis using an aquatic organism such as pondweed'. The traditional method uses counting bubbles of oxygen or measuring the gas produced using pondweed, and schools may also wish to carry out this experiment to fulfil AQA's criteria. However, the practical given here has proved to be a more successful variant of investigating light intensity.

I   Compare the colours of all your bottles with those of the pH range bottles.

J   Record the pHs of the solutions in your bottles in a suitable table.

Recording your results

1   Record your results in the table below.

Distance from lamp to bottle (cm)	pH at start	pH at end	Rate of photosynthesis (change in pH/hour)

Considering your results/conclusions

2   **a**   For each bottle, calculate the rate of photosynthesis as the change in pH per hour. Algae also respire. Respiration produces carbon dioxide, which lowers the pH. Therefore only use values where the change in pH is positive.

change in pH = pH at end – pH at start

$$\text{rate} = \frac{\text{change in pH}}{\text{time (in hours)}}$$

    b   Use your calculations to complete the last column of the table above.

3   Plot your results on a scatter graph. Plot the variable that you have changed (the independent variable) on the *x*-axis. Plot the rate of photosynthesis on the *y*-axis.

Considering your results/conclusions

4 **a** Describe the pattern shown on your graph.

b Explain why this pattern is observed.

5 H Light intensity can be calculated using the inverse square law. Calculate the light intensity for each distance using the formula Light intensity = $1/d^2$ where d is the distance from the lamp to the bottle of algae.

Sketch the shape of the graph of light intensity on the x-axis and rate of photosynthesis on the y-axis.

Evaluation

6   Explain the purpose of the tube covered in foil.

Exam-style questions

01.1   Green plants are able to make their own food.

Complete the sentences below, using the words from the box.   **[3 marks]**

oxygen	transpiration	hydrogen	photosynthesis
nitrogen	respiration	carbon dioxide	

Green plants use light energy to produce their own food by absorbing _____ gas from the

air and water from the soil. _____ gas is released as a by-product. The process is called

_____.

01.2   What measurements would you need to take to calculate the rate of photosynthesis?   **[2 marks]**

01.3   Sodium hydrogencarbonate can be used to increase the amount of carbon dioxide in the water surrounding pondweed.

Describe a method you could use to investigate the effect of carbon dioxide concentration on the rate of photosynthesis. Use the apparatus in the diagram below in your method.

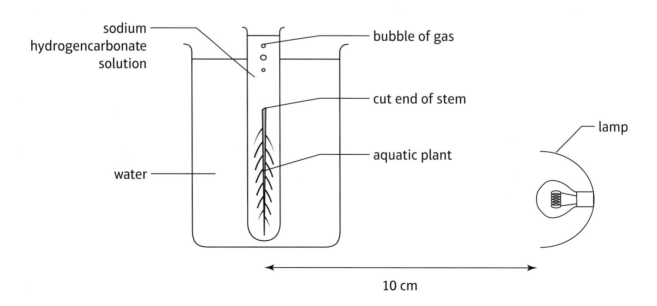

sodium hydrogencarbonate solution

bubble of gas

cut end of stem

aquatic plant

lamp

water

10 cm

You should include:

- how you will change the independent variable
- how you will control other variables.   **[6 marks]**

01.4   The graph shows the effect of light intensity on the rate of photosynthesis at two different concentrations of carbon dioxide (CO_2).

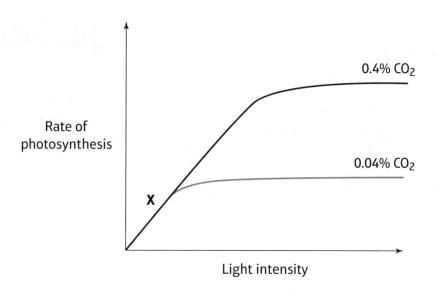

Suggest which factor is limiting the rate of photosynthesis at point **X**.   **[1 mark]**

01.5   Explain why the rate of photosynthesis increases when the carbon dioxide concentration is increased.   **[1 mark]**

We need to respond to changes in our environment. Sometimes these responses need to be rapid so that we are protected from an imminent threat, for example an object travelling towards us very quickly. The time taken for us to react is known as our reaction time. You are going to undertake a simple investigation into reaction times. You will need to analyse the results to see if faster reaction times can be linked to skills or experiences, e.g. being proficient at reactive computer games.

Your teacher may watch to see if you can:

- follow instructions carefully
- work safely.

Core learning outcomes: I am able to…
select appropriate apparatus and techniques to measure the process of reaction time
safely and ethically use humans to measure physiological function of reaction time and responses to a chosen factor.

Method

A The person who is having their reactions tested should sit down on the chair with their weaker arm (not the one they normally write with) placed on the table. Their hand should be overhanging the table edge.

B The tester holds a ruler vertically between the outstretched index finger and thumb of the person being tested. The finger and thumb should not be touching the ruler. The top of the thumb should be level with the zero mark on the ruler.

C The tester releases the ruler without telling the person being tested. The person being tested has to catch the ruler as quickly as possible.

D When the person catches the ruler, record the number that is level with the top of their hand. Record the length of the drop in the table below. Repeat the drop five times and calculate an average.

E Now swap roles and repeat steps **A** to **D**. If your group is larger than two, repeat the steps for each person.

F Find out who has the fastest reaction time.

Practical Objective

To find out who has the fastest reactions.

Content Objective

The nervous system allows humans to react to their surroundings and coordinate their behaviour.

Apparatus

- metre rule
- bench or table
- chair or stool
- a partner

Safety
- When the ruler is falling, it could fall in different directions. Take care that it does not hit anyone.

Ruler measurements (cm)				
Drop	Person 1	Person 2	Person 3	Person 4
First drop				
Second drop				
Third drop				
Fourth drop				
Fifth drop				
Average drop				

Considering your results/conclusions

1 Draw a suitable graph or chart to show your results.

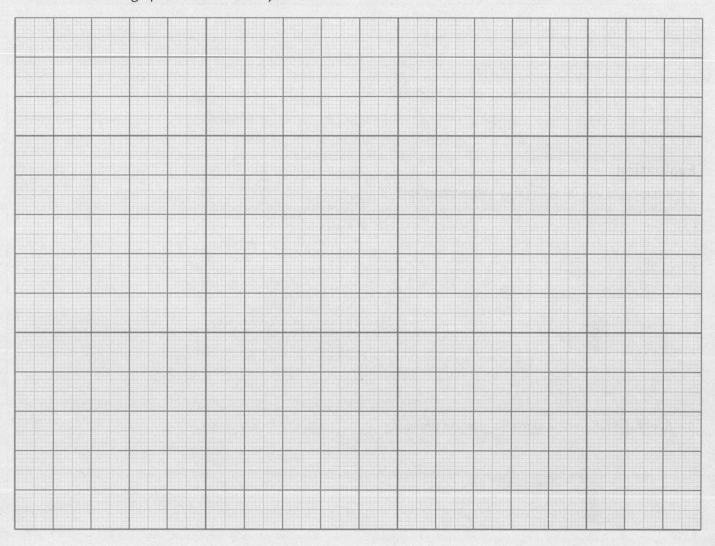

2 **a** Who has the fastest reaction time? Explain your answer.

b Is there any reason why this person has the fastest reaction time?
(Hint: Think whether this person plays lots of video games or is good at sports with fast reaction times.)

3 Did the reaction times increase or decrease from the first drop to the fifth drop? Explain any pattern you can see in your results.

Evaluation

4 What could you do to improve this experiment?

5 Suggest a different way to test reaction times.

Exam-style questions

01.1 All nervous control systems are made up of receptors, coordinators and effectors.

Draw in lines to show which of the boxed items on the right is a receptor, coordinator or effector. **[3 marks]**

Receptor	Brain and spinal cord
Coordinator	Cell in retina of the eye
Effector	Pancreas
	Muscle in the arm
	Nerve cell in finger tip

01.2 Your reaction times can be measured by using a computer program. One example of how this works is by having to click when a box changes from red to green.

A student wants to compare reaction times using this computer program.

Suggest which **three** variables need to be controlled. **[3 marks]**

1 _____

2 _____

3 _____

01.3 Give a reason why some males would have difficulty spotting the colour change. **[2 marks]**

_____

_____

Responding to a stimulus by growing towards or away from it, is called a tropism. A tropism caused by light is a phototropism. A tropism towards a stimulus is a positive tropism. Plant shoots are positively phototropic, so the plant gets enough light for photosynthesis. Plant roots are negatively phototropic. You are going to investigate the principle of positive phototropism using seedlings exposed to different amounts of light.

Your teacher may watch to see if you can:

- follow instructions carefully
- work safely.

Core learning outcomes: I am able to…
use appropriate apparatus to record length and time
select appropriate apparatus and techniques to measure the growth of shoots or roots
safely and ethically use plants to measure physiological function of growth in response to light or gravity
observe biological specimens to produce labelled scientific drawings.

Hypothesis

Write down your hypothesis. You might draw a diagram to explain your hypothesis.

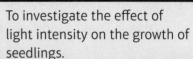
Practical Objective

To investigate the effect of light intensity on the growth of seedlings.

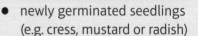
Content Objective

Plants produce hormones, which control their growth and response to light.

Apparatus

- newly germinated seedlings (e.g. cress, mustard or radish)
- Petri dishes
- ruler
- light source
- water
- box
- compost, cotton wool or folded kitchen towels

Method

You need to plan an experiment to test your hypothesis. Use the following questions and the suggested apparatus list to help you write a plan. Ask your teacher to check your plan before you carry out your investigation.

- How many seedlings will you use in each experiment?
- How will you alter how much light the seedlings receive?
- What control experiment will you set up?
- What variables do you need to control?
- What possible risks or safety issues could arise during this experiment?
- How will you measure growth? You need to do something that generates a value so you can compare seedlings.
- How will you use the apparatus? Draw a labelled diagram to help explain your answer.

Safety

- Wash hands after handling compost.
- Take care if using scissors.

1 Write your plan in the space below. Include a labelled diagram of your apparatus.

Considering your results/conclusions

2   Draw a results table in the space below.

3 Draw a suitable graph to show your results, with the independent variable on the *x*-axis and the dependent variable on the *y*-axis. The independent variable should be something to do with light intensity (although it might be linked with time). The dependent variable should be something to do with height or general growth of the seedlings. Remember to include a key.

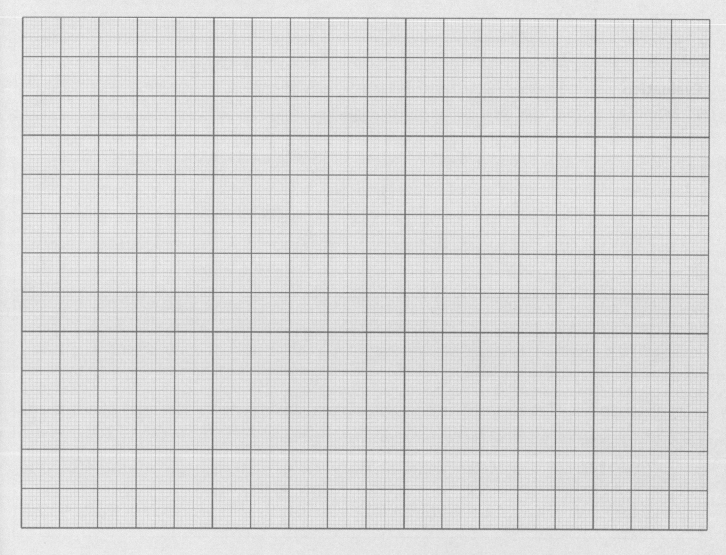

4 What conclusion can you make about the effect of light intensity on the growth of seedlings?

5 Why should you have used multiple seedlings?

6 Do your results support your hypothesis?

Evaluation

7 Describe a way in which you could improve your experiment.

Exam-style questions

01   Plants produce a hormone called auxin.

A student sets up an experiment to investigate the effect of directional light on seedlings.

This is the method used.

1.   Two groups of 10 seedlings were placed in a sealed cardboard box.
2.   A hole was cut in the right-hand side and a lamp placed next to the hole.
3.   For one group of seedlings, the shoot tips were covered.
4.   For another group of seedlings, the shoot tips were not covered.

After three days, the student used a protractor to measure the angle of the seedlings. In the table below, straight (vertical) is zero, growth towards the light is positive and growth away from the light is negative.

	Change in angle from vertical (degrees)									
Covered seedlings	0	0	+1	0	−1	0	0	0	0	0
Uncovered seedlings	+10	+8	+12	+20	+15	+11	+16	+17	+9	+6

01.1   Explain why 10 seedlings were used in each group.   **[1 mark]**

01.2   Explain the results for each set of seedlings.   **[4 marks]**

01.3   What is the advantage to the seedling of this response to directional light?   **[2 marks]**

A transect is used to study the distribution of organisms and how it is affected by changes in environmental conditions. With a belt transect, quadrats are placed at regular intervals along the transect line to sample the organisms. You will use a belt transect to study the effect of abiotic factors on the abundance of low-growing plants. The transect will stretch between open ground and heavy shade under a large tree. Several abiotic factors will vary along the transect. Before you start, you will need to decide which abiotic factors to measure and how to measure them. You will also need to decide which plants to record and how you will record their abundance within each quadrat.

Your teacher may watch to see if you can:

- work efficiently
- follow safety guidance.

Core learning outcomes: I am able to…
use appropriate apparatus to record length and area
use transect lines and quadrats to measure distribution of a species
safely and ethically use organisms to record their response to a factor in the environment
apply appropriate sampling techniques to investigate the distribution and abundance of organisms in an ecosystem via direct use in the field
use appropriate techniques in more complex contexts including continuous sampling in an investigation.

Method

A You are going to investigate the distribution of a particular plant species. Choose from: dandelions, daisies or buttercups. (Your teacher might suggest an alternative plant that is found in the local area.) If your teacher has not told you where to place the transect, look for somewhere that shows obvious variation in environmental conditions, such as from bright light to deep shade under a tree, or from an area that shows heavy trampling to an area with less trampling.

B Decide which environmental factors you will measure and how you will measure them.

C Peg out the tape measure along the ground to form the transect line.

D Take measurements at regular intervals along the transect line (as shown in the diagram). Decide on your measurement intervals, which may depend on how long the line is and how much time you have to record information.

E Place the top left-hand corner of the quadrat at a measurement point on the transect line.

F Measure the environmental factors at that point and record them.

G Record the abundance of your selected organism (this is the plant species you chose earlier) in the quadrat.

H Repeat steps **F** and **G** at each measurement point along the transect.

Practical Objective

To investigate the distribution of a species using a transect and quadrats.

Content Objective

Ecologists use a range of methods with transects and quadrats to determine the abundance and distribution of species in an ecosystem.

Apparatus

- long tape measure (at least 20 m) with pegs at each end
- quadrat (e.g. 50 cm × 50 cm square)
- apparatus for measuring suitable abiotic factors, e.g. light sensor and recorder, soil humidity sensor, anemometer (wind speed measurer)
- *optional:* identification charts and pencil

Safety ⚠

- Follow any safety guidance related to the working area.
- Consider the safety aspects of your chosen site, such as poisonous plants, animal faeces or open water, and take appropriate precautions while working.
- Wash your hands after the experiment.

Recording your results

1   In the space below, draw a table to record the abundance of the organism you sampled at each point along the transect line as well as the environmental factor measurements at each point.

2 Draw a suitable chart or graph to show your results.

Considering your results/conclusions

3 Describe the change in distribution of your chosen organism along the transect.

4 Describe the change in your chosen environmental factor along the transect.

5 Describe any correlation between the change in distribution of the organism and the change in environmental factor.

6 Suggest an explanation for any correlation that you have described in question **5**.

Evaluation

7 Describe an experiment you could do in the lab to test whether the environmental factor you measured affects the organism as you suggest in your answer to question **6**.

Exam-style questions

01   A lawn weed killer will kill broad-leaved weeds but not grass.

An area of lawn was divided in two, with one half treated with lawn weed killer.

This is the method used.

1.   In each area, a student laid out two tapes at right angles to form axes.
2.   A calculator was used to generate random numbers for coordinates.
3.   A quadrat was placed at each pair of coordinates.
4.   The number of dandelion plants in each quadrat was counted.

01.1   Why were the sites of the quadrat chosen at random?   **[1 mark]**

01.2   Calculate the mean number of dandelions per quadrat in the treated lawn. Write your answer in the table below.   **[1 mark]**

Quadrat number	Number of dandelion plants	
	Treated lawn	**Untreated lawn**
1	2	6
2	0	4
3	1	7
4	0	3
5	0	5
6	1	8
7	5	1
8	0	3
9	2	9
10	1	6
Mean number of dandelions per quadrat		5.2
Estimated total number of dandelions in area of lawn		4160

01.3   The area of the quadrat is 0.25 m². Each area of lawn is 200 m².

Calculate the estimated number of dandelions in the treated lawn. Write your answer in the table above.   **[2 marks]**

01.4   How effective was the lawn weed killer? Explain your answer using results from the investigation.   **[3 marks]**

Microorganisms are an important part of an ecosystem because they are decomposers: they break down dead organisms and animal wastes in a process called decay. The decomposers release enzymes that break down complex molecules in the dead organisms to simple molecules. These simple molecules can then be used by the decomposers and other organisms. Decay is naturally slow – certainly too slow to be observed during a lesson – so you are going to model the process in milk.

Your teacher may watch to see if you can:

- follow instructions carefully
- work safely.

Core learning outcomes: I am able to…
use appropriate apparatus to record temperature and pH
measure rate of decay by pH change.

Hypothesis

Write down a hypothesis for this investigation and explain it.

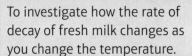

Practical Objective

To investigate how the rate of decay of fresh milk changes as you change the temperature.

Content Objective

Changes in temperature, water and oxygen availability affect the rate of decay of biological material.

Apparatus

- full fat milk
- lipase solution
- beakers
- small syringes
- Cresol red
- stop clock
- sodium carbonate solution
- test tubes with rack
- stickers or pen
- two thermometers
- one for the water bath and one for the test tube containing the milk
- water baths at three temperatures
- ice

Safety

- Take care not to burn yourself on hot liquids.
- Sodium carbonate solution is an irritant.

Method

The decay of milk is a slow process (compared to the length of a typical lesson) so you are going to model decay in milk using an enzyme called lipase. In nature, the fall in pH would be caused by the formation of lactic acid. In this experiment, the fall in pH will be mainly due to the formation of fatty acids. However, this experiment does produce a quick result which can be analysed.

A Set up two test tubes in the test tube rack, one containing $5\,cm^3$ of lipase and the other containing $5\,cm^3$ of milk. Label the two tubes using stickers or a pen.

B Add five drops of Cresol red solution to the test tube containing milk. Cresol red is an indicator that is purple in alkaline solutions but becomes yellow when the pH drops below 7.2.

C Add $7\,cm^3$ of sodium carbonate solution to the milk test tube. The contents should be purple. Place a thermometer in the test tube.

D Place both test tubes in the same water bath. Place another thermometer in the water bath and wait until the temperature of the solution in the test tube reaches the temperature of the water bath. Record the temperature of the water bath.

E Use a pipette to add $1\,cm^3$ of lipase to the milk mixture.

F Start the stop clock.

G Gently stir the milk mixture (using the thermometer) until it turns yellow. Record the time taken for the colour to change.

H Rinse out the test tube that contained the milk mixture. Once it is clean, add $5\,cm^3$ milk, five drops of Cresol red solution and $7\,cm^3$ sodium carbonate solution.

I Repeat steps **D** to **H**, using a different temperature water bath each time. Use ice to create a cold water bath.

J You could share your results with other members of the class, so you have a greater range of results.

Considering your results/conclusions

1 Record your results in the table below. There are additional columns so you can record results from other groups.

Temperature of milk (°C)	Time taken for milk mixture to turn yellow (seconds)			
	Group 1			Mean

2 Draw a suitable graph to show your results, with the independent variable (the temperature of the milk) on the *x*-axis and the dependent variable (the time taken for the milk mixture to turn yellow) on the *y*-axis.

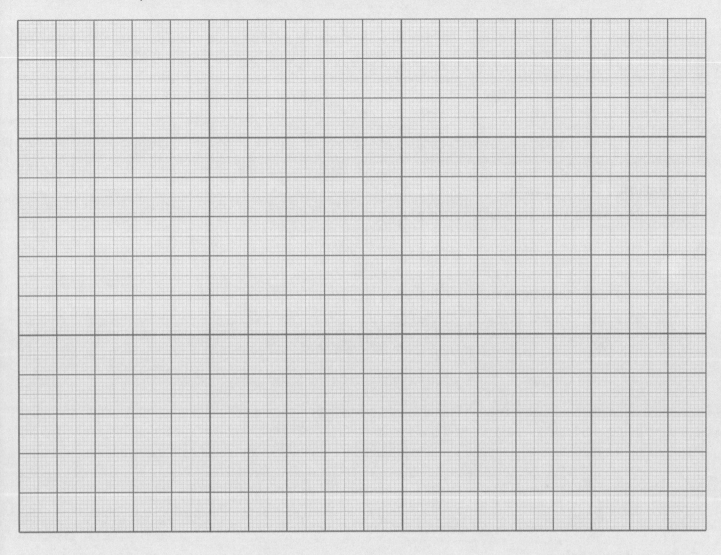

3 The milk in the test tube is slightly alkaline to start with (purple colour). As the milk decays, acids are produced, turning the indicator yellow. What can you conclude from your results about the relationship between temperature and the rate of acid production?

4 Do your results support your hypothesis?

5 Did temperature affect the rate of change in pH of the milk mixture? Explain your answer.

Evaluation

6 Describe a way in which you could improve your experiment.

Exam-style questions

01 The methylene blue test is used to judge the quality of raw milk. As the number of bacteria in milk increases, the concentration of oxygen falls. Methylene blue changes colour as oxygen levels fall.

[high oxygen concentration] ⟶ [low oxygen concentration]

blue ⟶ colourless

This is the method used.

1. Add $10\,cm^3$ of the milk sample to a test tube.

2. Add $1\,cm^3$ of methylene blue indicator solution to the test tube and mix well with the milk.

3. Seal the test tube and place in a water bath at 37 °C.

4. Record how long it takes for the colour to change.

01.1 Explain why the concentration of oxygen falls as the number of bacteria in the milk increases. **[2 marks]**

01.2 Explain why the test tubes must be sealed. **[1 mark]**

01.3 What colour will the milk and methylene blue mixture be in step **2**? **[1 mark]**

01.4 What colour will the milk and methylene blue mixture be at the end of step **4**? **[1 mark]**

01.5 As the bacteria grow they release lactic acid, which lowers the pH of the solution. The pH of the solution can be measured with a pH probe.

Suggest why this may be a better method than using the methylene blue test. **[2 marks]**

01.6 A student carried out the test with UHT long-life milk. The methylene blue had not changed colour after eight hours. Explain why this was so. **[1 mark]**

Word	Meaning
accuracy	How close a value is to its real value.
anomalous	Does not fit a pattern.
caution	Means 'beware'.
coarse focusing wheel	The wheel on a microscope that moves parts of the microscope a large amount to get the image in focus.
column graph	Another term for 'bar chart'.
control variables	Variables whose values need to be kept steady during an investigation.
correlation	A relationship between two variables. If an increase in one is linked to an increase in the other, it is 'positive'. An increase in one linked to a decrease in the other is 'negative'.
data	Observations or measurements collected in investigations.
decimal places	The number of digits after the decimal point.
dependent variable	The variable that is measured in an investigation. The values of the dependent variable depend on those of the independent variable.
directly proportional relationship	A relationship between two variables where one variable doubles when the other doubles. The graph is a straight line through (0,0). We say that one variable is directly proportional to the other.
discrete data	Data given in the form of limited values. For example, shoe sizes come in whole sizes and half sizes but not in sizes in between. So size 4, size 4½ and size 5 are all possible, but size 4.149 is not. The number of different shoe sizes is limited.
estimate	An approximate answer, often calculated from a sample or using rounded values.
evidence	Data used to support an idea or show that it is wrong.
hazard	Something that could cause harm.
hazard symbol	A warning symbol that shows why something can cause harm.
hypothesis	An idea about how something works that can be tested using experiments. The plural is *hypotheses*.
independent variable	The variable that you chose the values of in an investigation.
interval	The gap between one value of an independent variable and the next, in an investigation.
linear relationship	A relationship between variables that produces a straight line when plotted on a scatter graph. The line does *not* have to go through the (0,0) point.
line graph	A graph used to show how a variable changes with time.
line of best fit	A line going through a set of points on a graph, so that roughly equal numbers of points end up on either side of the line.
mean	An average calculated by adding up the values of a set of measurements and dividing by the number of measurements in the set.
median	The middle value in a set of values that has been written in order.
mode	The most common value in a set of values.
model	A way of showing or representing a phenomenon that helps you to think about it or to investigate it.
outlier	Another term for 'anomalous reading'.
peer review	An evaluation of the quality of a scientific paper carried out by other scientists who conduct research in the same area of science.
precision	How close a set of repeated measurements are to one another.
prediction	What you think will happen in an experiment.
qualitative data	Data that is not in the form of numbers (e.g. the names of colours).

random error	A mistake made in a measurement, which can be different every time that measurement is made.
range	The highest and lowest values in a set of data.
relationship	A link between two variables.
repeatable	Results that are similar when repeated by the same experimenter. You can be more certain that a set of repeatable results is correct.
reproducible	Results that are similar when repeated by different experimenters.
risk	The chance of harm being caused by a hazard.
sample	To take a small part of something to investigate. You use a sample to draw conclusions about the larger whole.
scatter graph	A graph in which data for two variables are plotted as points. This allows you to see whether there is a relationship between the two variables.
significant figures	The number of digits of a value, starting from the first non-zero digit.
specimen	The part of a sample studied using a microscope.
systematic error	An error that is the same for all readings, such as forgetting to zero a balance before using it to measure a series of masses.
theory	A hypothesis (or set of hypotheses) that has been repeatedly confirmed through experiment and for which there is a high degree of agreement in the scientific community.
trial run	A quick, rough version of an experiment that is carried out to ensure that the main experiment is designed well.
variable	Anything that can change and be measured.

1 Microscopy

Drawings for Methods 1, 2 and 3. Cells should be drawn with a sharp pencil and clean lines. Labelling lines should be drawn with a ruler and should not overlap. Your writing should be neat. The magnification or scale should be added to show the size of the cells.

Exam-style questions

01.1 Cell wall – F (1)

Cytoplasm – D (1)

01.2 chloroplast (1)

01.3 Convert to micrometres by multiplying by 1000. (1)

This might be done before or after finding a sixth of the length of the cell.

divide length of cell by 6 (1)

give answer to 3 significant figures = 16.7 µm (1)

01.4 2.6 µm (1)

2 Microbiology

1–3 Your own results.

4 There are areas of no growth (clear regions) around the antiseptic discs. This shows that the antiseptics prevent bacterial growth.

5 **a** Your own answer and explanation.

b This is the antiseptic with the largest clear region about it.

6 Your own answer and reason.

7 **a** Aseptic techniques include: flaming the neck of the culture bottle; lifting the lid of the Petri dish as little as possible; using tweezers/forceps to handle the discs.

b It is important to work aseptically to prevent the introduction of contaminants (e.g. other types of bacteria) which could affect the results.

Exam-style questions

01.1 (percentage) concentration of handwash (1)

01.2 0 (1)

01.3 So they knew how many bacteria there were without the handwash, to compare the control results with the handwash results. (Look for more than just 'to compare'.) (1)

01.4 all the repeated results are close to the mean (1)

01.5 range between 75% and 100% (1)

01.6 at 100% all bacteria are killed, but at 75% some are still alive (1)

3 Osmosis

1 Your own prediction.

2–5 Your own results.

6 Mean calculated from your results.

7 Your own graph.

8 The potato slices that gained mass did so because water moved by osmosis into the root from the surrounding solution. The potato slices that lost mass did so because water moved by osmosis from the root into the surrounding solution. Any potato slices that didn't change mass would have been in a solution with the same solute concentration as the potato cells.

9 Percentage change removes any variation due to differences in initial mass between slices.

10 Calculating a mean takes away or reduces the impact of any possible anomalous results which could be caused by variations between the potatoes.

11 Your own suggestion.

12 Divide the change in mass by the length of time the potatoes were left in the sucrose solution.

Exam-style questions

01.1 4 cm³ of stock sodium chloride solution (1)

6 cm³ distilled water (1)

01.2 sodium chloride solution is more dilute than cytoplasm of cell (1)

water moves from sodium chloride solution into cell (1)

by osmosis (1)

01.3 onion cells have a cell wall which prevents the cell from bursting (1)

01.4 water may move into blood by osmosis and burst blood cells (1)

glucose and salts may diffuse out of blood into dialysis fluid (1)

4 Food tests

1 Your results will depend on the foods supplied and tested. The table shows some typical results.

Food	Iodine test	Benedict's test	Biuret test	Emulsion test
full-fat milk	yellow–orange	yellow	purple	cloudy
whey	yellow–orange	bright blue	purple	clear
egg white	yellow–orange	bright blue	purple	clear
potato	black–blue	bright blue	light blue	clear
glucose	yellow–orange	red precipitate	light blue	clear
(icing sugar)	yellow–orange	bright blue	light blue	clear

2 Your answers will depend on the foods supplied and tested.

3 Both the test for reducing sugars and the test for proteins could give an indication of the quantity of substance present, based on the colour produced.
In the test for reducing sugar, the colour changes from light blue (no reducing sugar) to green/blue, then orange and eventually red (lots of reducing sugar). This gives an indication of the amount of reducing sugar present.
In the protein test, the purple colour produced will be more darker the more protein is present.

4 This will depend on the results obtained if they were not as expected. Errors are most likely to occur if equipment is not cleaned properly between tests and food becomes contaminated with another sample. Therefore, it would be a good idea to ensure equipment (e.g. glassware, spatulas etc.) is cleaned between tests. Using coloured foods may make some colour changes more difficult to see. To overcome this problem, select foods that have neutral or muted colours.

Exam-style questions

01.1 solution 1 went blue/black with iodine

idea of getting a positive result with iodine (1)

01.2 (maximum 6 marks)

Level 3: A detailed and coherent explanation is provided which uses relevant data from the tables and comes to a conclusion consistent with the reasoning.	5–6 marks
Level 2: An attempt to use some data to come to a conclusion. The logic and use of data may be inconsistent at times but builds to a coherent argument.	3–4 marks

Level 1: Discrete relevant points made. The logic may be unclear and the conclusion may not be consistent with the reasoning.	1–2 marks
No relevant content.	0 marks

Indicative content:

Conclusion that solution 2 is albumen (egg white) and solution 3 is amylase.

Points that may be used to support this conclusion:

- both solutions are proteins – give positive result with Biuret test
- enzymes are proteins
- amylase digests starch
- starch is broken down to sugars
- Benedict's solution tests for sugars
- mixture of starch and solution 3 gives positive result with Benedict's solution
- solution 3 breaks down starch to sugars
- mixture of starch and solution 2 gives negative result with Benedict's solution
- solution 2 has no effect on the starch.

5 Enzymes

1   Your own prediction and explanation.

2–3   Your own results. Make sure each of the column headings in your table is clear.

4   Your own graph.

5–6   Your own description and suggestion.

7   Qualitative: the test only tells you if there is starch present or not. It cannot show how much is present/left.

8–11   Your own answers.

Exam-style questions

01.1   Pepsin digested the protein (egg white) to amino acids, which are soluble. (1)

Accept:

- enzyme for pepsin
- breaks down for digested
- peptides instead of amino acids

01.2   no enzyme present to digest the protein (1)

01.3   to keep the volume constant/same as tube B (1)

01.4   Change the ratio of pepsin to water in tube A. Accept more detailed answers. (1)

01.5   Give marks for reasons and methods, not values.

pH 2

Reason – pepsin is produced in stomach and this is acidic. (1)

Method – add same volume of pH solution (buffer) to each tube. (1)

in range of 30–40 °C

Reason – near optimum or below optimum so will not denature. (1)

(If body temperature is given, it must have the idea that this is likely to be optimum temperature.)

Method – water bath at appropriate temperature. (1)

6 Photosynthesis

1–2   Your own results.

3   Your own graph.

4   Your own description and explanation.

5 H   Light intensity varies with distance according to the inverse square law. So, if you double the distance from the light source

(move the lamp away), the light intensity is $\frac{1}{2^2}$ or $\frac{1}{4}$ times the original intensity (it reduces to a quarter of the original value). If you halve the distance to the light source (move the lamp closer), light intensity is $\frac{1}{\left(\frac{1}{2}\right)^2}$ which is 4 times the original.

This is the pattern you should see in the graph. Take a measurement in the middle of your values and look at what happens when that result is doubled or halved to see if it fits the inverse square law. Plotting the rate of photosynthesis against the inverse squared distance from the source (1/distance²) should give you a straight-line graph.

6   To show that light is required for the algal balls to photosynthesise. No colour change should have occurred in the control bottle, proving that light is required by the algal balls.

Exam-style questions

01.1   carbon dioxide (1)

oxygen (1)

photosynthesis (words must be in this order) (1)

01.2   volume of gas collected (1)

in a set time – accept suggested period of time, e.g. three minutes (1)

01.3   (maximum 6 marks)

Level 3: A detailed and coherent description is provided which clearly describes how to change the independent variable. Other suitable variables are given with clear methods of how to control them.	5–6 marks
Level 2: An attempt is made to describe how to change the independent variable but lacks precision. Other variables are given and an attempt is made to describe how to control them.	3–4 marks
Level 1: Discrete relevant points made. Description of method may lack clarity.	1–2 marks
No relevant content.	0 marks

Indicative content:

independent variable – concentration of sodium hydrogen carbonate

- use different concentrations of sodium hydrogen carbonate in the water surrounding the plant
- change the solution completely at end of each experiment

Other variables:

- light intensity – keep same lamp at same distance
- pondweed – use same piece of pondweed in each experiment
- temperature – monitor temperature of water in beaker with thermometer / use a heat shield to prevent water getting warm

01.4   light intensity (1)

01.5   carbon dioxide (concentration) is no longer a limiting factor (1)

7 Reaction time

1   This is likely to be a bar chart. The dependent variable (the results) should be on the y-axis and the independent variable (the students taking part in the experiment) should be on the x-axis.

2   a   Your own answer.

   b   There could be a correlation between fast reaction times and skill at reaction sports (basketball, football, hockey or tennis for example). The same is somewhat true for video games but this does depend on the style of game being played.

3 Your results are likely to improve as you practise more and learn what to expect. But they will also plateau. You can only get so quick on this test without resorting to cheating (e.g. anticipating and closing your hand before the ruler is dropped).

4 Some possible ways to improve the experiment include: increasing the number of repeats to ten drops per person, changing the hand to see if there is a difference with the other hand, altering the dropping point of the ruler.

5 Use a computer program or app where you have to press a button when a light or image is displayed. This would collect all of the data and ensure that reaction times are correctly measured.

Exam-style questions

01.1 receptor – cells in retina of the eye (1)

coordinator – brain and spinal cord (1)

effector – muscle in the arm (1)

01.2 any three from: (3)
- use same computer
- same lighting conditions
- same time of day
- same age

accept other suitable answers

01.3 red–green colour blindness (1)

(sex linked) more common in males (1)

8 Plant responses

1 Your own plan.

2 Your own results.

3 Your own graph.

4 The results will depend on the investigation, but possible conclusions are: the greater the light intensity, the greater the growth (increased height of seedlings); or the seedlings grow in the direction of the light (they may have curved or bent towards the light source).

5 If you use more than one seedling, you can calculate an average value. This means the results are more reliable.

6 Your own answer.

7 There are many possible improvements, such as: use different intensities of light or different colours of light; repeat the investigation using a different type of seedling; follow the original plan but use more seedlings to obtain a better mean value.

Exam-style questions

01.1 to ensure results are repeatable – accept idea that some seedlings may die (1)

01.2 (maximum 4 marks)

Level 2: A detailed and coherent explanation is provided. The student makes logical links between clearly identified and relevant points that explain why the two groups of seedlings have different angles of growth.	3–4 marks
Level 1: Simple statements are made, but not precisely. The logic is unclear.	1–2 marks
No relevant content.	0 marks

Indicative content:
- auxin is made in top of shoot
- in covered seedling auxin moves to all parts of stem
- in uncovered seedling auxin accumulates on shaded side
- in covered seedling all parts of stem grow
- in uncovered seedling shaded side elongates and stem bends towards the light

01.3 leaves are nearer to light (1)

for photosynthesis (1)

9 Field investigations

1–7 Your own results/answers.

Exam-style questions

01.1 to avoid bias in the sampling (1)

accept idea of might choose areas with / without dandelions

01.2 1.2 (1)

01.3 multiply mean number in quadrat by 4 to find number per m² – 4.8 (1)

then multiply by 200 for number in total area, which equals 960 (1)

01.4 reduces number of dandelions (1)

but not all dandelions are killed (1)

may be more/less effective on other weeds (1)

10 Decay

1 Your own results.

2 Your own graph.

3 Acid production increases as the temperature increases: the warmer the milk, the more acid is produced/the more decay occurs. (Be aware, however, that if the temperature rises too high, the enzyme will be denatured and no acid will be produced.)

4 Your own answer.

5 Your own answer.

6 Possible improvements include: use a datalogger to monitor pH change; run the investigation with more temperatures.

Exam-style questions

01.1 oxygen is used in respiration (1)

more bacteria, more respiration (1)

01.2 so oxygen could not enter the tube from the air (1)

01.3 blue (1)

01.4 white (1)

01.5 pH probe gives a numerical reading (1)

change in colour is difficult to judge and pH probe avoids this (1)

01.6 no live bacteria in the milk as it has been heat treated and the heat treatment kills the bacteria (1)